The Cowpat-Throwing Contest
and other sporting poems

Collected by Brian Moses
Illustrated by David Pattison

HODDER
Wayland

For Pauline, Jean and the
Hastings Children's Book Group

Published in Great Britain by Hodder Wayland, a division of Hodder Children's Books

The right of Brian Moses to be identified as the author and David Pattison as the
illustrator of this Work has been asserted by them in accordance with
the Copyright, Designs and Patents Act 1988.

A Catalogue record for this book is available from the British Library.

ISBN 0 750 23130 0

Printed and bound in Portugal

Hodder Children's Books
A division of Hodder Headline Ltd
338 Euston Road, London NW1 3BH

Contents

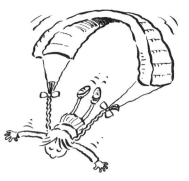

Acknowledgements

'The Cowpat-Throwing Contest' first published in
Knock Down Ginger and Other Poems,
Cambridge University Press, 1994.
Copyright © Brian Moses, 1994.

All other poems reproduced by kind permission
of the poets.

The Spider Eating Contest

Whoever thought this one up
must have been mad,
horribly wicked
or terribly sad.

The people who entered
were brave, but insane.
they were fearless and bold
and they didn't complain

But they *would* if they'd known.
they'd have scarpered in haste.
for with spiders, there's no
getting rid of the taste!

Andrea Shavick

7

The Very Heavy Wellie Triathlon

To get your wellies heavy
pour in each boot
two pots of glue, some school rice pudding
a dozen ball bearings, six tins of beans
two small spoonfuls of cement
and several litres of engine oil.

The course is tough
up the steeply sloping sand dunes
a scramble through the sucky mud
cross the stream on greasy tree trunk
hang on to your wellies!

Dive into the deep dark lake
quickly swim though savage swarms
of rubber eating welliefish,
jumping out you grab a bike
pedal ten kilometres
of twisted tracks and rutted roads
finally you reach the end
hang on to your wellies!

Not everybody makes it
the course is covered with contestants
who lost their wellies in the mud
who crunched their toes on cold baked beans
who could not kick and keep afloat
who could not balance on their bike
in other words, the fallers and the failures
whose wellies were too heavy.

Go for gold
hang on to your wellies!

David Harmer

The Bugs Bite Back!

The Animal Soccer League:
Thousands came
To Bugs versus Elephants –
A vital game.
Bugs overwhelmed at first
By Elephants' power:
Twenty behind
In half an hour.
Elephants' display
Absolutely brill:
At half-time leading
Twenty-six – nil.
Manager of Bugs
Doesn't scream;
Talks softly to
Downhearted team:
'You're playing well.
They're playing better.
We're only short of
A goal-getter.
Striking power
Is what we need
And so – I'll bring on
Millipede.'

Second half
Transformation!
Bugs have total
Domination.
Inspired by rampant
Millipede,
Bugs turn on
A goal stampede.
Run out winners
Twenty-seven – twenty-six.
Millipede
Scores five hat-tricks.
Bugs' manager
Interviewed on TV
Is quizzed about his policy:
'Substitution
Really smart –
But why didn't Millipede
Play from the start?'
Replies, 'Of course
He would have done.
But he took till half-time
To get his boots on.'

Eric Finney

Bag Flinging

Introducing the noble art of –
School bag flinging.
Two friends
Stand exactly shouting distance apart.
On the word 'GO'
School bags are simultaneously flung
Across the shouting distance

And caught.

World record at time of writing,
Forty-nine consecutive flings.
But

On the fiftieth fling
The two school bags
Met – mid air
fell fast

Ba⋯
Suffered only minor cuts and bruises
But Bag B
Lay lifeless

A concussed carrier
With a split zip
Through which a broken ruler poked.
There were serious internal injuries;
A lacerated lunch box
(With complications)
Perforation of the yoghurt pot;
With consequent leakage over
The adjacent football shorts.

Bag B's final fling.

John Coldwell

Pushy Peas

I'm pushing a pea up Snowdon,
I'm pushing it there and back,
I'm pushing it with my nose-tip,
I'm trying to get the knack.

I'm pushing a pea up Snowdon,
I'm crawling on hands and knees,
The judges are strict and sniffy,
They send you home if you sneeze.

One nostril's packed with pebbles,
The other one's blocked as well,
I'm pushing a pea up Snowdon,
It's wrecking my sense of smell.

I pushed a pea up Snowdon
Through blizzards and gales and snows,
I didn't quite beat the record,
I was pipped at the post – by a NOSE!

Clare Bevan

The Inside-Out Olympics

Hello! And welcome to our games
The famous SCIPMYLO
Where everything's turned inside-out
Come on – let's watch the show!

The hurdles get crawled under
And the sprint is really slow
The long jump's actually quite short
The high jump's rather low

The discus never leaves your hand
The relay's back-to-front
The shot-putt feels as light as air
While javelins are blunt

The divers climb onto the board
The swimmers don't get wet
And every race starts with the words
'Go! On your marks! Get set!'

All the athletes long to lose
The highest score is nil
In fact, the winners tend to be
The ones who just stand still!

Katherine Bright

The Pigtail Parachute

It's a dangerous sport
a bit of a hoot,
using your pigtails
as a parachute.

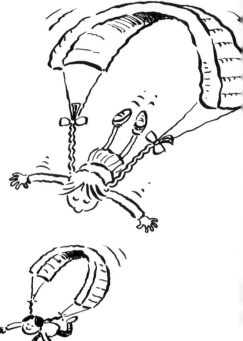

But people still do it,
they fall through the air
with just a parachute
tied to their hair.

Straight hair is best,
that's what they say,
for hair that's curly
just gets in the way.

16

Thin hair is dangerous
and if it's frizzy
it can quickly unravel
to send you dizzy.

So get those pigtails
into the air,
tie a parachute
onto your hair.

Fly high above
your own ceiling
and just enjoy
that floating feeling!

Andrew Collett

The Cowpat-Throwing Contest

Malc and me and Ian Grey, we couldn't believe
when we heard someone say, that in cattle towns
of the old Wild West, they held cowpat-throwing contests!

How awful, how dreadful, what if it hit
you smack in the mouth, you'd gag, you'd be sick,
but we knew, even then, the day would come when we'd try it.

And it wasn't very long after that when the three of us
were sent away – 'Get out of the house,
get out of my sight, go somewhere else and play.'

And we walked until the houses stopped, looked
over a hedge and there in a field were pancakes of
the very stuff we'd been talking about for days.

The cows looked friendly so we started up
with a chunk or two that might have been mud
but we knew we'd move on to the slimy stuff before long.

18

Malc was the first to try it out and scooped up
a really terrible lump, but while Ian was yelling
and backing away, he tripped and sat down in the dung.

Malc was laughing fit to burst and he must have forgotten
his hands were full till he dropped the lot
all down his trousers, then wiped his hands on his shirt.

I made the mistake of grinning too till Malc hit my jacket
and Ian my shoes, and I watched it spreading everywhere,
while the cows just stood there and mooed!

Well, after that it was in our hair and down our jumpers
and everywhere. Our fingernails were full of the stuff,
then Ian said, 'Pax, I've had enough.'

'We look awful,' Malc said, 'and we smell as sweet as
a sewage farm in the midday heat. We shouldn't have done it,
we've really been daft' – but Ian just started to laugh.

We laughed up the lane while a cloud of flies
trailed us back to Ian's place, where his mum's grim face
soon shut us up as she fixed her hose to the tap.

'It's history, Mum, it's really true. It's what they did
in the Wild West—' but we lost the rest of what he said
as a jet of water pounded his chest.

Then water was turned on Malc and me, and we both went home
in Ian's clothes, while his mum phoned ours and tried
to explain just what it was that we'd done.

I knew my mum would have a fit. 'That's it,'
she said, 'the final straw. No way you're going out
to play for a week, no, a month maybe more.'

'Get in that bath, use plenty of soap, how could you be
such a silly dope? Use the nail brush too and wash
your hair. I'll be in there later to check.'

I scrubbed and I brushed but I couldn't make the smell
disappear, and I wondered how the cowboys coped
when their contest was done and everyone climbed in the tub.

And kids held their noses and called out, 'Pooh!'
for days and weeks and months after that, but it didn't matter,
we'd proved we were best, not at spellings or sport
or school reports, but at cowpat-throwing contests.

Brian Moses

Sweeping the Country

The name isn't very snappy,
We're trying to think up another.
It's the best sport ever invented – it's
How Far Can You Fling Your Brother?

Frances Nagle

Counting Sheep Competitions

One problem
with competing
in the
sport of
Counting Sheep
is, that
everyone who
tries it
tends to
fall aslee...

Mike Johnson

23

Cherry Stone Spitting

Tinker went first, and took a pot shot
Tailor thought he had it all sewn up
Soldier waited for the order to spit
Sailor was blown off course by a sudden gust
Richman had a servant to spit for him
Poorman gave it all he had – which wasn't much
Beggarman asked if he could have another go
But Thief – had run off with the prize.

Paul Bright

Sumo Wrestlers

Sumo wrestlers
Grab folds of flesh
Pink as old pyjamas,
And heave and grunt
On the soft, white square
Of their playpen.

And when they hitch up
Their huge nappies,
And when their squashy faces
Crumple with pain,
They seem to me
Like the lost babies
Of beanstalk giants.

Clare Bevan

Tossing the Pud

In my home village,
if the weather's good,
there's an annual event
called Tossing the Pud
when Christmas puddings,
all large and round,
on Christmas Eve,
thud hard on the ground.

The aim of this rather
peculiar sport
(and the winner is given
a bottle of port)
is getting your pudding,
with a bit of luck,
clear over the roof
of the *Whistling Duck*.

It's worth spectating
on Christmas Eve,
when villagers shove,
and thrust, and heave.
But watching it all
takes a lot of pluck,
and if something comes whistling down –
then *duck!*

Barry Buckingham

Camel Wrestling

Welcome to the camel wrestling,
It's just getting interesting.
Ahmad versus El Amin,
Either one of them could win.

Ahmad's camel looked aloof
until it got him with his hoof.
See the slobber and the spit?
That camel is a lunatic.

Ahmad's camel flails and kicks,
but El Amin brings his down quick.
Ahmad pauses to recover.
El Amin brings down another.

El Amin has now floored four!
Ahmad evens up the score!
The camels all put up a fight.
Ouch! That was a nasty bite.

Camels fall like tubs of lard.
Can a draw be on the cards?
That's the lot. They're out of time.
Ahmad eight, El Amin nine.

Ahmad's right down in the dumps,
You can see he's got the hump.
And the camels? You can tell,
Wrestling makes them mad as El.

Jane Clarke

Advice for Staging your own Olympic Games

Never play volleyball with a bag of flour
Never use Mum's hair brush as a baton in the relay race
The flower bed is not a sandpit for the long jump
And remember – the Olympic Games does not include kiss-chase

Never pole-vault in the vicinity of Grandpa's greenhouse
Never throw the discus using Mum's best plates
The broom handle is not a pole – nor is it a javelin
Never use flowerpots (especially if they have flowers in) for
                                                        weights

Your dog is a dog, not a horse
Although, at a push, could be used for equestrian events
Do not use the duvet covers in the airing cupboard
To make those big marquee-type tents

Never use *The Complete Set of Delia Smith* for the winners
                                        podium
Never bribe the judges with crisps, chocolate, football cards
                                      or cash.
And finally when Mum comes home to find her house and
                                garden in a mess,
Say Excuse me, but I'm in the hundred metres – must dash!

Roger Stevens

Gerbil Juggling

Gerbil juggling is such fun
and kinder than eating them in a bun.
The champion can juggle twelve and his cat.
Look at him go… oh dear…

splat.

*Please note: No gerbils have been harmed in the
preparation of this poem.*

Tim Pointon

Prize Spy

At the spies' sports day,
spies try to win prizes,
for fake beards and noses
and secret disguises.
This year's 'Prize Spy' champ
to claps, cries and cheers,
applies his disguises
and just – disappears!

Liz Brownlee

Supermarket Slalom

On your marks
Get trolley. Go!
List in one hand
Starting slow
Veg for Sunday
Lunch for eight
Throw it in
Accelerate
Salad stuff
A bit of fruit
Concentrate
Don't lose the route
Box of rice
Some curly pasta
Really cruising
Moving faster
Take the turn
The castors squeal
Grab an instant
Curry meal
Missed an aisle
5 Penalties
Go back for
The frozen peas
Two old ladies
Stand and natter

34

Can't slow down
The grannies scatter
Pressure's on
No time to slack
At the check-out
Rush to pack
Bags full, sprinting
Out the door
Crowd goes crazy
Hear them roar
New world record!
What a star!
Give the champ
A chocolate bar!

Paul Bright

The Total Flop

(For high-jumper Dick Fosbury, who's famous Fosbury Flop won him Olympic gold in 1968)

In sport I'm for the high-jump,
No Fosbury, just a flop.
Dropped from the karate team,
They've given me the chop.

I've tried to throw a discus,
But only got disgusted.
Go-karted so slowly
That the engine parts all rusted.

I'm no good on tennis courts,
I can't stand the racket.
I've done with computer sports,
Given up, can't hack it.

I hurt my neck while batting,
Should've know I'd crick it.
Football is my habit,
Though I wish that I could kick it.

Had a go at snooker
But my game has gone to pot.
Yachting wasn't right for me –
I felt an idi-yacht.

I did a bit of fencing
But merely caused a fence.
Tried to lift a hundred pounds,
But only raised ten pence.

Hold on, though, I think at last
My bad luck's going to stop.
They're hanging out their rugby shirts
And want me for a prop.

Nick Toczek

37

The Girning Contest

I can pull out my bottom lip over the top;
Puff out my cheeks till they practically pop;
Wrinkle my forehead and then cross my eyes:
How I yearn for the Champion Girner prize.

The day of the contest one man from the south
Arrives with his nose tucked inside his mouth,
His ear-lobes curl till they turn inside out,
His face looks, at best, like a petulant trout.

At the end of the contest I know I've not won:
The Champion Girner, when all's said and done,
Pulls the ugliest face. And he's ugly as sin.
So everyone cheers and welcomes his win.

He accepts the gold trophy, enjoys all the fuss,
Then the Champion Girner goes home on the bus.
As it drives down the road, the man waves to the crowd.
Though his face is contorted he clearly looks proud.

Only I, as I glance in my bus-driver's mirror,
Discover the secret behind this year's winner.
That man is no girner, I soon realise:
It's the face he was born with that won him the prize.

Celia Warren

The Cowboy's Cowpat Tossing Day

They gathered cowpats down in California, USA
selecting nice, dry, flat ones for cowpat tossing day.
Gnarled men tossed them, baked hard by the Californian sun
and cattle wandered here and there producing fresher ones.
Women, watching men compete pressed hankies to their noses
and cowboys swaggered, wafting strange aromas (not of roses)
Dogs attacked the cowpats as they skimmed above the ground
mistaking them for frisbees and men chased the thieving hounds.
Children played with cowpats amidst mothers' cries of wrath
and were dragged off screaming loudly and then driven home to bath.
The winner cheated and the contest ended in a fight
and then a celebration which went on for half the night.
And then they galloped down the trail with caterwauls and hoots,
reached their homes at dawn and went to bed, still in their boots.

Marian Swinger

40

The Camel Wrestler's Coach Observes

Getting a camel to wrestle
Is not so very hard...
Once you've managed to get it
Into its leotard.

Philip Waddell

The Great Eating-Jelly-Through-a-Straw Contest

Under starters orders now –
Stand by your jellies!
Straws up!
They're off!

And Hosepipe Annie's in the lead…
But only half a lick behind is Jack the Gulp.
He's overtaking!
And on the outside Gargling Lil is guzzling
Faster than a blowtorch melting snow.
Wow. It's neck and neck –
Just watch that jell-o go!

They're in their stride now.
Slurping solid. Suck and pucker all the way –
Vacuuming that slippy slop
Right up.

Stop! Stop! The referee has pulled the plug.
Gargling Lil is gulping down her final glug.
Jack's had it. Out of it. The paramedics think it's jelly-shock.
And Annie wins the day!!!!

The crowd goes wild:
Their cry goes up –
Oh, Annie! You are the nation's favourite child.
Let fanfares blare! Let fireworks flare!
Let golden flags and banners be unfurled
For Hosepipe Annie –
Jelly-Eating Champion of the World!

Jan Dean

Horses are Harder to Tread on

Bored –
So we found
Two snails,
Named Laura and John
And started a race.

An hour later
The contestants
Had yet to move.
For some reason
They seemed stuck
In a groove.

So, we offered incentives –
Orange slices at half-time,
A free trip
To the rubbish heap,
Double portions of grass –
But Laura and John were unwilling
To budge.

So, Tom gave his a nudge –
But I felt sorry
For John
And put him back
In the hedge. 'Race over –
my snail's the champ –
I've won,'
Declared Tom.

Till Dad,
Not looking,
Came up the path
And trod
On the winner.

That's when
We gave up snail racing.
Horses are harder to tread on.

Pie Corbett

Conker Contest

It helps to be bonkers
when you're playing conkers,
for such is the luck of the draw,
if your conker is weak,
you will find that technique
doesn't do much to even the score.

There's no point in cheating,
as that's self-defeating,
they'll check that your conkers aren't baked,
or pickled for days
in ingenious ways,
or made out of concrete and faked.

So come on, get whacking,
it's time to get cracking
and fight to the death. This is war!
All your hopes will be dashed
if your conker is smashed –
conquered conkers can conquer no more.

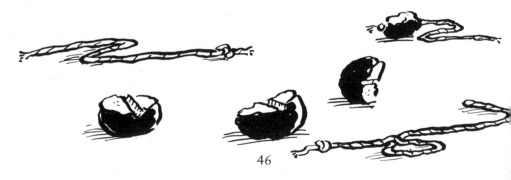

Now knuckles are battered
and conkers are shattered,
the losers are all feeling sore.
The conker we cheer
is a thirty-three-er,
and the winner? The boy from next door.

Jane Clarke

Octopus Wrestling

Ref, it's not fair –
he's pulling my hair.

He's got my arms up my back
and my knees just went crack.

Ref, it's really not fair –
he's still got four tentacles to spare.

Tim Pointon